First published in Great Britain 2023 by Farshore
An imprint of HarperCollins*Publishers*
1 London Bridge Street, London SE1 9GF
www.farshore.co.uk

HarperCollins*Publishers*
Macken House, 39/40 Mayor Street Upper, Dublin 1, D01 C9W8

ISBN 978 0 0086 1253 5
ISBN 978 0 0085 4759 2
Printed in Italy
1

A CIP catalogue record for this book is available from the British Library.

MIX
Paper | Supporting
responsible forestry
FSC
www.fsc.org
FSC™ C007454

This book is produced from independently certified FSC™ paper
to ensure responsible forest management.

For more information visit: www.harpercollins.co.uk/green

# CONTENTS

x5

Spoink   Zigzagoon   Zangoose   Zoroark

# The Reunion

Ash and Pikachu's journey continues in this busy town as they hope to reunite Dark-type Pokémon Zorua with Zoroark. Can you find the illusion fox in the scene or is it just too quick?

x5

Lotad *x2*        Roselia *x2*        Grovyle *x2*

# Happy Hoenn

Pikachu is excited to make some new friends here in the Hoenn region. The group is ready to explore and have an adventure on this vast island. Can you find these pairs in the happy scene?

Meditite *x3*    Loudred    Shuppet

**x7**

# Sleepy Village

All the adventures have caught up with Pikachu, who now needs a nap! Surrounded by friends, Pikachu has a rest in this sleepy Hoenn village. What else can you see among the roofs?

Buizel

x4

# Sinnoh Shaymin

It's a beautiful day here in the Sinnoh region. Ash and Pikachu continue their adventure here in search of the Grass-type Mythical Pokémon, Shaymin. Can you find it and these other Pokémon?

Turtwig   Piplup   Shaymin   Croagunk   Sudowoodo

Geodude

Shaymin    Pachirisu    Feebas    Whiscash    Psyduck

## Waterfall Fun

The sound of this Sinnoh waterfall relaxes Pikachu after a battle against a mighty Magnemite. But there might still be some opponents to defeat. Find these Pokémon in and around the river.

| x4 | # Arrival on Unova |
|---|---|

Purrloin    Excadrill    Scolipede    Darumaka

# Arrival on Unova

Ash and Pikachu have just landed in the Unova region. They are excited to discover the unknown Pokémon that populate this place, including Watchog, who is wary of the new visitors!

Deerling x4

x3    x8

# Deep in the Forest

The Unova region has many forests in and around its famous cities. They are a great place to find Grass-type and Bug-type Pokémon. How many can you find hidden in the trees?

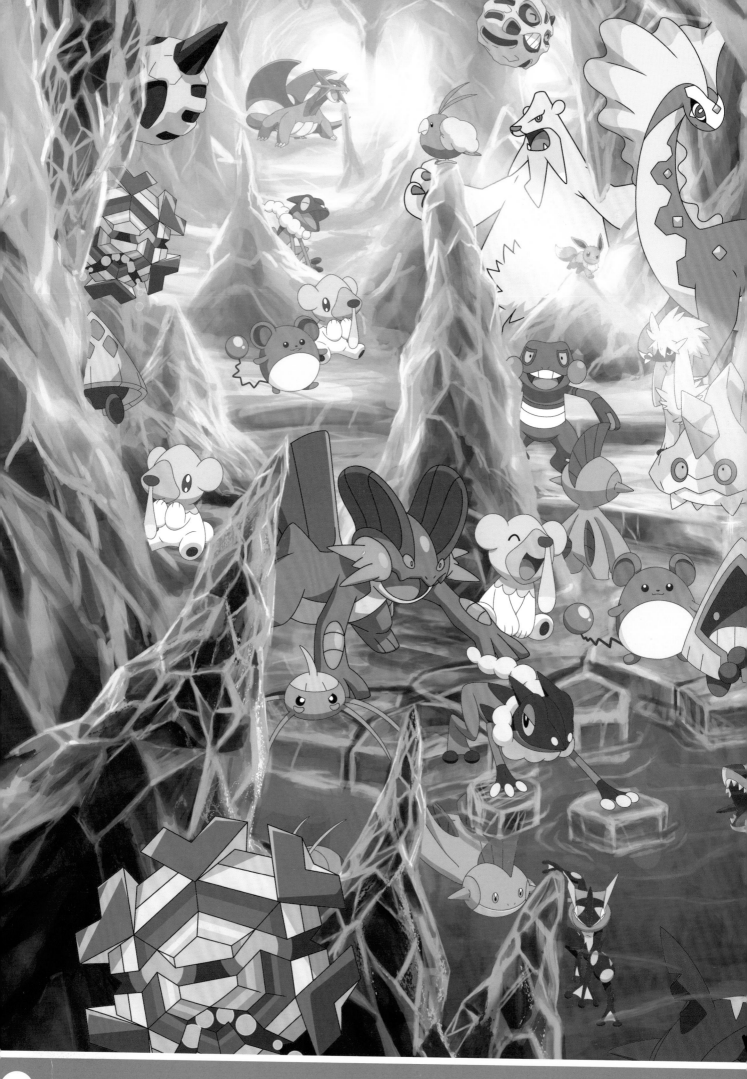

# A World of Ice

Ash's Pikachu has made his way to the Kalos region, where a frozen ice palace awaits! Froslass sleeps peacefully while the other Pokémon party. Who can you spot in this frosty scene?

Surskit *x2*

Eevee

Froslass

Espeon | Sableye *x3* | Umbreon

## A Spectacular Sight

The night sky in the Kalos region is something to behold! Pikachu meets many nocturnal Pokémon at this incredible gathering. Find Umbreon and more in the crowd.

**x6**

Alola Grimer *x2*    Bounsweet    Pichu *x3*

# A Strange Encounter

The Alola region is made up of five islands, each with their own guardian. Ash and Pikachu are surprised when they are greeted by Tapu Koko, the guardian of Melemele island.

Alolan Sandshrew    Alolan Vulpix *x5*    Tapu Bulu

**x6**

# Mountain Mayhem

Ash and Pikachu move on to the island of Ula'Ula, where they end up on top of a snow-covered mountain. It's the perfect locaton for Ice-type Pokémon. Who can you spot in the snow?

**x4**

# Galar Gallop

Ash's Pikachu has made it to the Galar region, the final destination of his epic journey. All his friends are ready for a race, but can anyone beat the mighty Galarian Ponyta?

Wooloo          Sirfetch'd          Gossifleur *x2*

x5

Rookidee *x2*   Thievul   Impidimp

# The Adventure's End

Night has fallen on the Galar region, and Pikachu is ready to go home. Every new region was full of surprises and amazing friends to be found. Find these final Pokémon to complete your adventure!

# ANSWERS

**4**

*Kanto Sunset*

**6**

*Playtime at the Park*

**8**

*Ships Ahoy!*

**10** The Reunion

**12** Happy Hoenn

**14** Sleepy Village

**16** Sinnoh Shaymin

**18** Waterfall Fun

**20** Arrival on Unova

# ANSWERS

**Deep in the Forest**

**A World of Ice**

**A Spectacular Sight**

**28**

*A Strange Encounter*

**30**

*Mountain Mayhem*

**32**

*Galar Gallop*

**34**

*The Adventure's End*